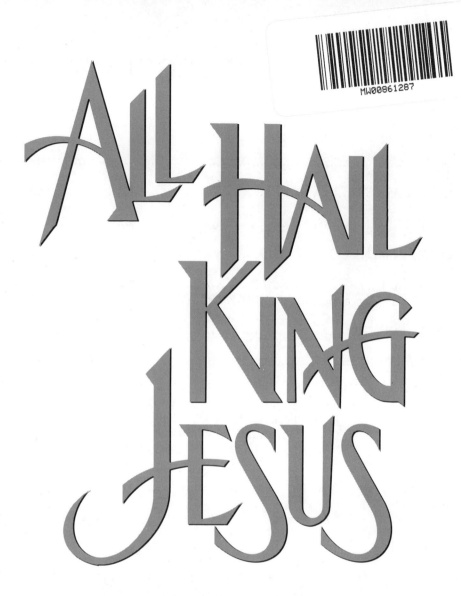

All Hail King Jesus

An Easter Choral Celebration

by Marty Parks

Lillenas PUBLISHING COMPANY

KANSAS CITY, MO 64141

COMPANION PRODUCTS

BOOK ME-41

STEREO CASSETTE TA-9138C

ACCOMPANIMENT CASSETTE MU-9138C

ACCOMPANIMENT COMPACT DISC MU-9138T

REHEARSAL TAPES MU-9138R
    4 cassettes, 1 per voice part, in a vinyl binder

SERVICE FOLDERS ME-41SF

ORCHESTRATION OR-9138

Flute I, II	*Cello*	*Tuba*
Oboe	*Double Bass*	*Percussion I, II*
Clarinet	*Trumpet I, II, III*	*Harp*
Violin I, II	*French Horn I, II*	*Rhythm (piano, bass, drums)*
Viola	*Trombone I, II, III*	*Conductor's Score*

Music engravings by Wayne Yankie

CONTENTS

All Hail King Jesus

D. M.

Boldly, with majesty! ♩ = ca. 84

DAVE MOODY
Arr. by Marty Parks

6

Star! Through-out all e-ter-ni-ty I'll sing His prais - es; And for-ev - er-more I will reign with Him.

CD: 03

All hail King Je - sus; All hail Em - man - u - el! King of Kings, Lord of Lords, Bright Morn - ing Star! Through - out

rall.

NARRATOR: *(without music)* All hail King Jesus! All hail Emmanuel!

(Music begins) Will we ever understand a love so amazing that the King of Heaven, the Lord of Glory, would become a man, clothed in human flesh, and die in our place, for our sins?

When we consider so great a sacrifice, when we recognize His splendor and majesty, and when we experience His unending mercy and grace, we bow before Him and cry from the depths of our soul, "All hail King Jesus!"

Interlude I

(All Hail King Jesus)

DAVE MOODY
Arr. by Marty Parks

NARRATOR: *(without music)* Three years of ministry had passed. The reputation of this teacher, healer, and miracle worker preceeded Him wherever He went. Approaching Jerusalem during His final days, Jesus was honored as King. Pressing around Him, a large crowd called out, "Hosanna! Hosanna to the Son of David!" And as they chanted, the words of the psalmist were fulfilled before their eyes: *(music begins)*

SCRIPTURE VOICE: Lift up your heads, O you gates... that the King of Glory may come in. Who is this King of Glory? The Lord Almighty... He is the King of Glory! (Ps. 24:7,10)

Lift Up Your Heads

with Hosanna, Loud Hosanna

S. L. F.

STEVEN L. FRY
Arr. by Marty Parks

to the com - ing King. Bow be-fore Him

and a - dore Him; sing.

To His Maj - es - ty let your prais - es

14

sang; Through pil - lared court and tem - ple the love - ly an - them rang. "Ho - san - na in the high - est!" That an - cient song we

giv - ing glo - ry to the King___ of Kings,

To the King___ of___ Kings!

NARRATOR: *(without music)* As we celebrate the resurrection of Jesus, we are reminded that His triumph cannot be separated from His atoning work on the cross. Only a pure and sinless substitute would suffice, and so, the King became a lamb… *(music begins)* the holy Lamb of God.

SCRIPTURE VOICE: In Him we have redemption through His blood, the forgiveness of sins, in accordance with the riches of God's grace. (Eph. 1:7) We who once were far away have been brought near through the blood of Christ. (Eph. 2:13) Worthy, worthy is the Lamb.

Worthy, Worthy Is the Lamb

Marty Parks
BASED ON REV. 5:12

*ANONYMOUS

With dignity ♩ = ca. 88

CD: 08

mp

⑤

p 1st time: Sopranos (opt. solo)
mp 2nd time: Sop. and Alto

⑨ Adoringly

Wor - thy, wor - thy   is   the Lamb;   Wor - thy, wor - thy

p – mp

⑬

is___ the Lamb;   Wor - thy, wor - thy   is   the Lamb

*Accompaniment derived from Canon in D by Johann Pachelbel.

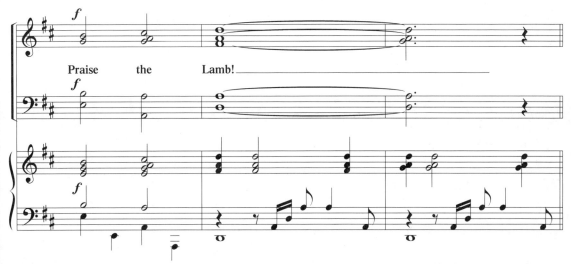

Praise the Lamb!

SCRIPTURE VOICE: "Worthy is the Lamb who was slain, to receive power and wealth and

27 CD: 11 Lightly
sub. *mp*
simile

wisdom and strength and honor and glory and praise!" (Rev. 5:12) "You are worthy…

31 because You were slain, and with Your blood You purchased men for God from every tribe and

language and people and nation." (Rev. 5:9) Worthy is the Lamb!

CD: 12
mf
rall.

NARRATOR: *(without music)* The eternal purpose of an Almighty God found its fulfillment in a pure and spotless Lamb. Centuries before, prophets had foreseen this event. One fateful night, as Jesus was praying in the garden, a large detachment of soldiers, together with a group of officials from the chief priests and Pharisees, approached Him there. *(Music begins)* They sought out the one Judas called "Master" and with no resistance they seized Him.

*SCRIPTURE VOICE: He was oppressed and afflicted, yet He did not open His mouth; He was led like a lamb to the slaughter, and as a sheep before her shearers is dumb, so He did not open His mouth.

NARRATOR: The armed guards hurried Jesus to the house of Caiaphas, the high priest, who, with the elders of the people, felt threatened by Jesus' claim to authority and by the throngs that followed Him. There they ridiculed Him, hurling insults and false accusations.

SCRIPTURE VOICE: By oppression and judgement He was taken away. For He was cut off from the land of the living; for the transgression of my people He was stricken.

NARRATOR: Led before Pilate, the Roman governor, the Savior of the world was subjected to brutal scourging as He endured the blasphemous abuse of cruel soldiers.

SCRIPTURE VOICE: Yet it was the Lord's will to crush Him and cause Him to suffer.

NARRATOR: Wanting nothing to do with this man, Pilate presented Him to an angry mob who called out for His death. "Here is your King!" he said. But the crowd shouted, "Take Him away...crucify Him!" "Shall I crucify your King?" Pilate asked. But they screamed more insistently, "We have no king but Caesar. Crucify Him...crucify Him!" Fearing what might result if he took no action, Pilate shouted his proclamation: "Away with Him! Let Him be crucified!"

SCRIPTURE VOICE: *(after music has stopped)* For He bore the sin of many, and made intercession for the transgressors.

(segue immediately to "The Iniquity of Us All")

Scriptures on this page adapted from Isaiah 53.

The Arrest...The Trial...The Sentence

MARTY PARKS

Slowly and mysteriously ♩ = ca. 58

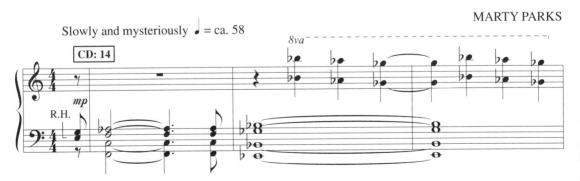

The Iniquity of Us All

M. P.
Based on Isaiah 53

MARTY PARKS

With mystery ♩ = ca. 94

1st time: Ladies unison
2nd time: Men unison

1. He was de - spised by men, re - ject - ed,_____
2. He was wound - ed for all our trans - gres - sions;_____

A man of sor - rows and ac - quaint - ed with
He was bruised for our in - i - qui -

grief. And the Lord has laid on
ty.

Him, The Lord has laid on Him the in -

30

O Calvary's Lamb

C. B., B. G. and T. G.

Slowly and gently ♩ = ca. 63

CHARLES BOSARGE, BILL GEORGE and TOMMY GREER

Arr. by Marty Parks

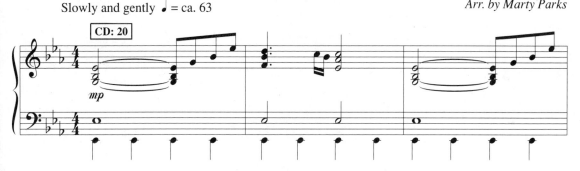

1st time: Alto solo
2nd time: Tenor solo

Worshipfully

This fal-t'ring tongue____ would dare to speak____ of Thee, my
eyes____ at last shall see____ Thy ho - ly

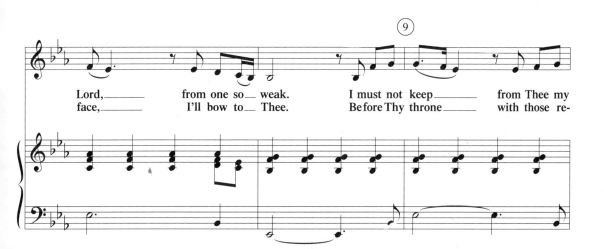

Lord,____ from one so__ weak. I must not keep____ from Thee my
face,____ I'll bow to__ Thee. Before Thy throne____ with those re-

praise;_____ for Thy glo - ry I will lift my voice and

deemed,_____ un - to Thee, O Lord, I'll lift my voice and

Both times: Duet (14)

mf

sing.

sing.

mf

(14)

mf

O Cal- v'ry's Lamb,   O Righ-teous One,   for sin - ners

(18)

died_____ whose sins were none;_____ All that I have,   all that I

(18)

am,_____ I owe to Thee,_____ O___

Cal - v'ry's Lamb.

CD: 22 Tenor solo *mp*

D.S.

And when mine

D.S.

36

38

SCRIPTURE VOICE: *(with music)* For God so loved the world that He gave His one and only Son, that whoever believes in Him shall not perish but have eternal life. (John 3:16)

NARRATOR: Eternal life…made possible only through the One who humbled Himself and endured suffering, shame and death on the cross. And when He had died, scripture tells us that He was laid to rest not in a grave befitting a mighty monarch, but in a borrowed tomb.

(after music has ended) But He arose. The empty tomb his followers discovered early that morning proclaimed to them — and still proclaims to us — that forevermore Jesus had conquered death and the grave. He had risen!

Interlude II
(All Hail King Jesus)

DAVE MOODY
Arr. by Marty Parks

Now and Forevermore

M. P.

MARTY PARKS

Wor - thy, Wor - thy, King of Kings and Lord of Lords!

Wor - thy is the Lamb of God,_____ Now and for - ev - er -

more!_____ The earth breaks its si - lence, in

All cre - a - tion sings:

54 *"Christ, the Lord, Is Risen Today" (Charles Wesley/Lyra Davidica)
Exuberantly

Christ, the Lord, is ris - en to -

day! _____

Now and for - ev - er - more! Ev - er - more!

Christ, We Do All Adore Thee

Medley

Worshipfully, with great expression

Arr. by Marty Parks

"Adoramus Te" from THE SEVEN LAST WORDS OF CHRIST (Theodore Dubois)

Christ, we do all a - dore___ Thee,

Freely ♩ = ca. 72

preferably unaccompanied to meas. 9

and we do praise Thee for - ev - er; Christ, we do all a -

dore Thee, and we do praise Thee for - ev - er!

For on the ho - ly cross hast Thou the world from sin re -

deem - ed. Christ, we do all a - dore Thee,

52

and we do praise Thee for - ev - er.

19 CD: 33 21

Unison mp "We Worship and Adore You" (Traditional)

We wor - ship and a -

Unison mp

19 Lightly, gentle rhythm 21

mp

dore You, Bow - ing down be - fore You,

56

with me to the end!

CD: 35

rall.

As in the beginning

Christ, we do all a - dore Thee, and we do praise Thee for -

NARRATOR: *(without music)* The King is alive! But what does that mean to us today? Will we claim this victory? Or do we live defeated lives? Perhaps the burdens of this very day have kept you from experiencing the joy He came to give.

It Is Finished

W. J. G. and GLORIA GAITHER

WILLIAM J. GAITHER
Arr. by Marty Parks

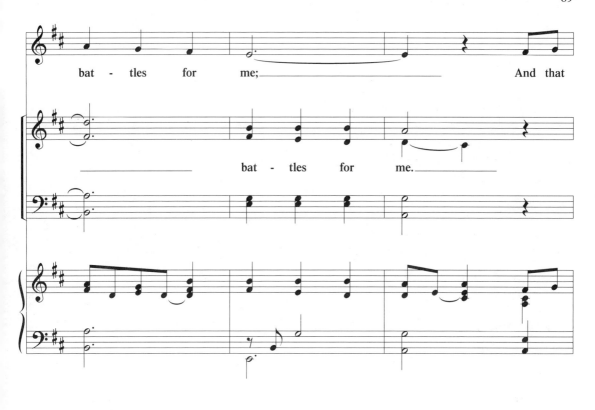

Joyously, with a triplet feel
Soloist join choir

fin - ished!_____ The bat - tle is o - ver!_____

It is fin - ished!_____ There'll be no more

war!_____ It is fin - ished!_____ The

72

SCRIPTURE VOICE: *(music begins)* Jesus said, "I am the resurrection and the life. He who believes in me will live, even though he dies. (John 11:25) I am the First and Last. I am the Living One; I was dead, and behold I am alive for ever and ever." (Rev. 1:17b, 18a)

NARRATOR: And one day we who have been redeemed will join thousands upon thousands of angels and every creature in heaven and earth, worshipping Him who sits on the throne. For the joy awaiting Him Jesus endured the cross…became a man obedient to death…and willingly gave His life for those He loved.

SCRIPTURE VOICE: But we see Jesus now crowned with glory and honor! (Heb. 2:9)

NARRATOR: …Exalted to the highest place, and given a name above every name…

SCRIPTURE VOICE: That at the name of Jesus every knee should bow…and every tongue confess that Jesus Christ is Lord! (Phil. 2:10, 11)

NARRATOR AND SCRIPTURE VOICE: All hail King Jesus!

Finale

Stately ♩ = ca. 58

Arr. by Marty Parks

CD: 46

* "Risen in Glory" (Parks)

22 Triumphantly ♩ = 100

Ris - en in glo - ry, Ris - en to reign!

22 With dignity

We bow be - fore Thee, The Lamb that was slain.

30
Unison
Crowned with glo - ry and hon - or, Crowned with wor - ship and
Unison
praise; With joy-ful al - le - lu - ias crown the
34
An - cient of Days!

CD: 47

decresc.

78

CD: 49

*All Hail King Jesus (Moody)

died, e - ter - nal life to bring and lives that

death may die! All hail King

Je - sus, All hail Em - man - u - el!

82